If I Listen With My Heart

I Hear the Savior's Voice

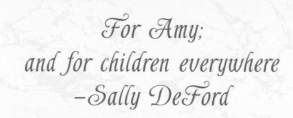

For Amy;
and for children everywhere
—Sally DeFord

Imagery © Greg Olsen. By arrangement with Greg Olsen Art Publishing, Inc. For information on art prints by Greg Olsen, please contact Greg Olsen Art Publishing, Inc., 208-888-2585.
Imagery © Liz Lemon Swindle. Courtesy of Foundation Arts. For print information, visit www.foundationarts.com.

Words to the song "If I Listen With My Heart I Hear the Savior's Voice" copyright © 2007 by Sally DeFord. All rights reserved.

Jacket and book design by Jessica A. Warner © 2011 Covenant Communications, Inc.

Published by Covenant Communications, Inc.
American Fork, Utah

Printed in China
First Printing: September 2011

18 17 16 15 14 13 12 11   10 9 8 7 6 5 4 3 2 1

ISBN 978-1-60861-375-5

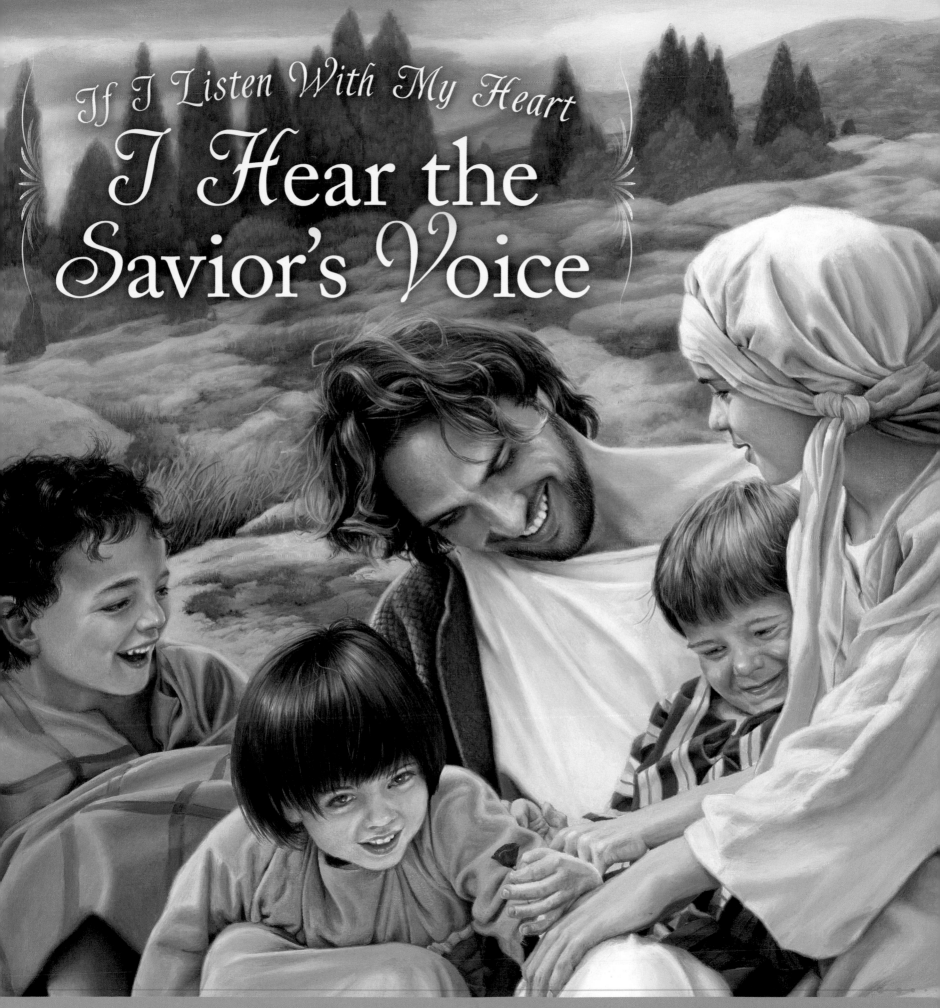

If I Listen With My Heart
I Hear the Savior's Voice

Words and Music by **Sally DeFord**   Artwork by **Greg Olsen & Liz Lemon Swindle**

If *I* had been

a little child

when *J*esus

lived on

earth,

I would have liked

to walk with *H*im

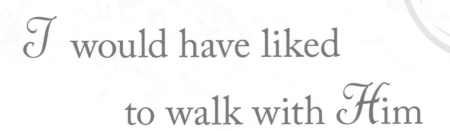

and listen to

*H*is words.

But as *I* search

the scriptures,

I can hear *H*is words of peace.

And if I listen
with my heart,
I hear the Savior's voice.

$\mathcal{I}$ hear a living $\mathcal{P}$rophet speak

the things that

$\mathcal{C}$hrist would say

If He were here

upon the earth

to talk with me

today.

The *Prophet*
teaches how to live
in righteousness
and peace.

lz lemon Swindle © 00

And if I listen
with my heart,
I hear the
Savior's voice.

I feel the
Holy Spirit
as He teaches
truth and right.

He comforts me
in times of need;
He testifies of Christ.

He speaks
to me in quiet ways
that fill my soul
with peace.

And if *I* listen

with my heart, *I* hear

the *S*avior's voice.

If I Listen With My Heart I Hear the Savior's Voice

Quietly

(Low-voice solo)

Sally DeFord

If I Listen With My Heart I Hear the Savior's Voice

Sally DeFord

Quietly (Simplified)

1: If____

I had been a____ lit - tle child when Je - sus lived on____ earth, I____ would have liked to
hear a liv - ing____ pro - phet speak the____ things that Christ would say if____ He were here up -
feel the Ho - ly____ Spi - rit as he____ tea - ches truth and____ right, He com - forts me in____

walk with Him and____ lis - ten to His____ words, But____ as I search the scrip - tures I can
on the earth to____ talk with me to - day, The____ pro - phet teach - es how to live in
times of need, He____ tes - ti - fies of____ Christ, He____ speaks to me in qui - et ways that

1 & 2

hear His words of____ peace,
right - eous - ness and peace, And if I____ lis - ten with my____ heart I hear the Sav - ior's voice.
fill my soul with peace,

3.

2: I____ hear the Sav - ior's voice.
3: I____

rit.

Original Version

If I had been a little child when Jesus lived on earth,
I would have liked to walk with Him and listen to His words.
But as I search the scriptures, I can hear His words of peace.
And if I listen with my heart, I hear the Savior's voice.

I hear a living prophet speak the things that Christ would say
If He were here upon the earth to talk with me today.
The prophet teaches how to live in righteousness and peace.
And if I listen with my heart, I hear the Savior's voice.

I feel my father's gentle hands laid softly on my head.*
I hear him call on priesthood power to comfort me in need.
I feel the warmth of heaven as he blesses me with peace.
And if I listen with my heart, I hear the Savior's voice.

He speaks to me in quiet ways that fill my soul with peace.
And when I listen with my heart, I hear the Savior's voice.

alternate lyric: I feel a priesthood holder's hands . . .

Note: These are the original words written for her daughter, Amy.